10-Minute Critical-Thinking Activities for Algebra

by

Hope Martin

J. WESTON

WALCH

PUBLISHER

Portland, Maine

User's Guide
to
Walch Reproducible Books

Purchasers of this book are granted the right to reproduce all pages where this symbol appears.

This permission is limited to a single teacher, for classroom use only.

Any questions regarding this policy or requests to purchase further reproduction rights should be addressed to:

Permissions Editor
J. Weston Walch, Publisher
321 Valley Street • P.O. Box 658
Portland, Maine 04104-0658

1   2   3   4   5   6   7   8   9   10

ISBN 0-8251-4343-8

Contents

To the Teacher

Critical-thinking skills include reasoning, predicting consequences, clarifying and assessing ideas, and judging the validity of an argument. Critical thinking in the mathematics classroom means finding patterns, solving problems in nontraditional settings, and analyzing change. We think of it as reasoning or thinking skills. Students who can think critically learn to examine results to "make sense of mathematics."

Algebra programs help students recognize and understand patterns, relations, and functions. Students learn to use algebraic symbols to represent and analyze mathematical questions. They learn to use mathematical models to understand quantitative relationships and to analyze change.

10-Minute Critical-Thinking Activities for Algebra is designed to

- promote problem solving and proportional reasoning

- develop basic mathematical concepts and skills

- encourage students to use patterns and analyze functions

- develop logical reasoning

- explore probability, statistics, and graphs

Students are asked to explain their reasoning and their problem-solving strategies. When students reflect on their problem solving, they develop mathematical and critical-thinking skills. They learn to assess the reasonableness of their answer, to consider other possible solutions, and to share their reasoning with other students. Students may discover other ways to solve a problem or more than one correct solution.

You and your students can take advantage of a *critical* 10 minutes every day. That adds up to 1,800 minutes a year, or about 40 additional mathematics classes over the course of a school year of 180 days! And who among us could not use eight more weeks of mathematics?

PART 1: Critical Thinking and Logic

As students sharpen and extend their skills, they learn to use inductive and deductive reasoning to formulate arguments. Thinking critically and reasoning logically are integral to doing mathematics.

In the first set of puzzles, students use Venn diagrams to describe and compare various elements of a problem. What these elements have in common or how they differ determines their placement in the overlapping circles. Students learn to read problems carefully to look for important information. They learn to distinguish the words *and, or, all,* and *only* to find solutions.

Students learn to read carefully and apply information from clues to solve matrix logic puzzles. It is a fun way to experience deductive reasoning.

To solve any of the puzzles, students must be well organized and their thinking must be precise. They must learn to work methodically. These reasoning skills—the same as those required to solve any problem—are transferable to other areas.

Choices for Lunch

A group of students was surveyed about their lunch preferences. Use the clues below to figure out how many students like hamburgers, hot dogs, and/or pizza for lunch. Of course, some students chose more than one of the foods. Some may have chosen all three! Place your answers in the appropriate sections of the Venn diagram.

- A total of 70 students were surveyed.
- 27 students like hot dogs.
- 26 students like pizza.
- 12 like hamburgers and hot dogs.
- 8 like hot dogs and pizza.
- 12 like only pizza.
- 3 like all three—hamburgers, hot dogs, and pizza.

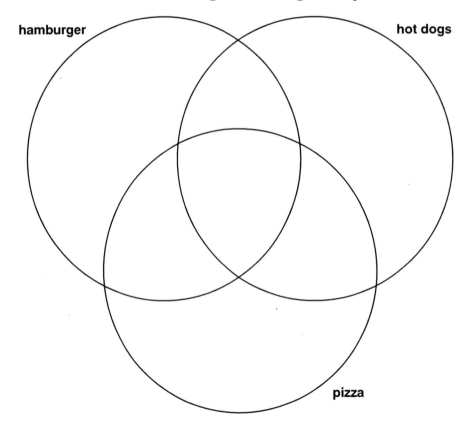

What Flavor Do You Like?

A group of students was asked about ice cream flavors. Use the clues below to figure out how many students said they liked peanut-butter chip, bumpy road, or tutti-frutti ice cream. Remember, some students chose more than one flavor. Some may have chosen all three! Place your answers in the appropriate sections of the Venn diagram.

- 47 students were asked which ice cream flavors they like.
- 10 like peanut-butter chip and bumpy road.
- 12 like peanut-butter chip and tutti-frutti.
- 8 like all three flavors.
- 25 like bumpy road, but
- 9 like only bumpy road.
- 30 like tutti-frutti.

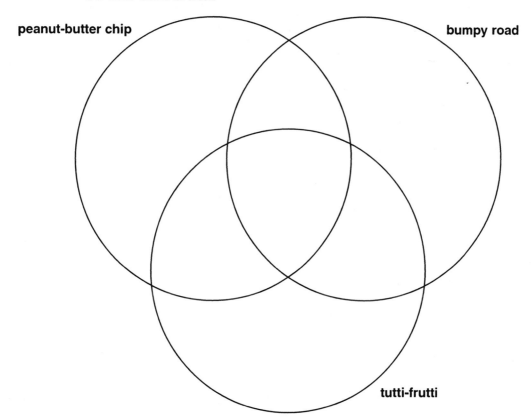

peanut-butter chip   **bumpy road**

tutti-frutti

The Mystery Venn

In the Venn diagram below, circle A and circle B have numbers that relate to each other in some way—but someone has forgotten to label them. How do the numbers in circle A relate to each other? How do the numbers in circle B relate to each other? How are the numbers shown in the intersection of the two sets related? Describe these relationships on the lines below.

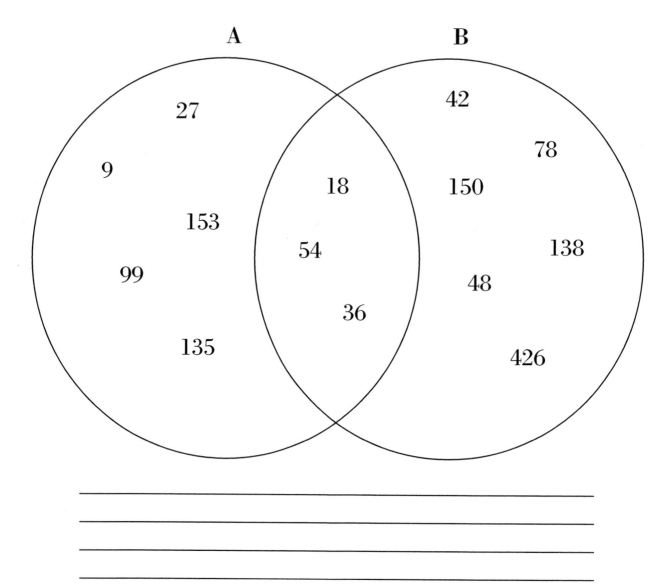

_____

_____

_____

_____

Where Were They Born?

Place each of these celebrities in the circle that **best represents** the place he or she was born.

Rod Stewart, musician, England

Leonardo DiCaprio, actor, Hollywood

George Foreman, boxer, Texas

Andy Rooney, columnist, New York

Edward Teller, physicist, Hungary

Cameron Diaz, actor, San Diego

Oprah Winfrey, TV star, Mississippi

Marion Jones, athlete, Los Angeles

David Bowie, musician, England

Martin Luther King, Jr., civil rights leader, Georgia

Vidal Sassoon, hair stylist, England

Princess Caroline, Monaco

E.T., visitor from outer space

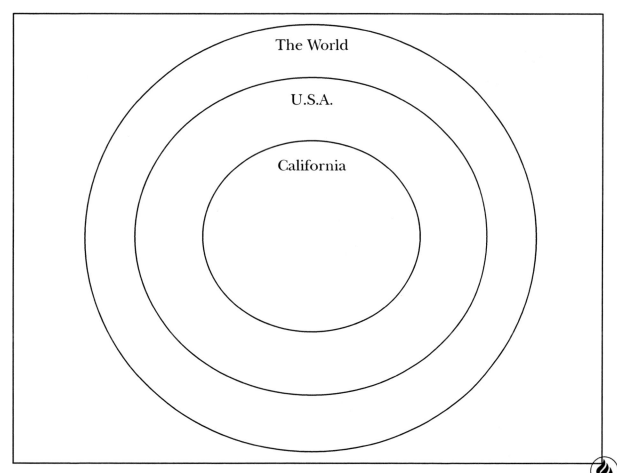

         10-Minute Critical-Thinking Activities for Algebra

Mystery Regions

Place each number in the correct region.

1. The number 6 appears in the triangle only.

2. The number 3 appears in the circle only.

3. The number 7 appears in the rectangle only.

4. The number 4 appears in the circle and triangle only.

5. The number 5 appears in the rectangle and triangle only.

6. The number 2 appears in the circle and rectangle only.

7. The number 1 appears in the circle, rectangle, and triangle.

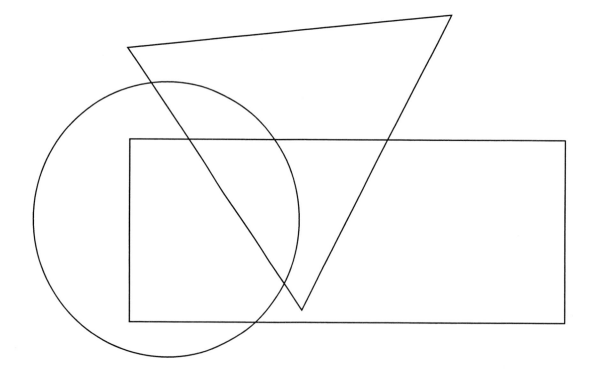

Cryptogram 1

Each letter below represents a different letter of the alphabet. To solve this puzzle, correctly substitute each letter and reveal a clever saying. If a letter appears more than once, it is like a variable and should be replaced by the same letter each time. Write your solution in the spaces above the letters.

Hint: Substitute a T for each Y, an S for each K, and an E for each C that appears in the puzzle. Now use your logic skills to solve this puzzle.

1. Y P C   T G C   R M I   Y T   E C

   K Z N N C K K S Z V   W K   Y T

   A C Y   T G   I T Z L   " Y L I " –

   N I N V C .

10-Minute Critical-Thinking Activities for Algebra

Cryptogram 2

Each letter below represents a different letter of the alphabet. To solve this puzzle, correctly substitute each letter and reveal a clever saying. If a letter appears more than once, it is like a variable and should be replaced by the same letter each time. Write your solution in the spaces above the letters.

Hint: Substitute a D for each X and an E for each Z that appears in the puzzle. Now use your logic skills to reveal this famous quotation.

2.   " W G U   A E M   X E   G X X C Y C E U ? "

     Y D Z   J D C Y Z   H M Z Z U   G B T Z X .

     " J D G Y ' B   E U Z   G U X   E U Z   G U X

     E U Z   G U X   E U Z   G U X   E U Z

     G U X   E U Z   G U X   E U Z   G U X

     E U Z   G U X   E U Z   G U X   E U Z ? "

     " C   X E U ' Y   S U E J , "   B G C X

     G V C W Z .   " C   V E B Y   W E M U Y . "

                         V Z J C B   W G K K E V V

Cryptogram 3

Each letter below represents a different letter of the alphabet. To solve this puzzle, correctly substitute each letter and reveal a clever saying. If a letter appears more than once, it is like a variable and should be replaced by the same letter each time. Write your solution in the spaces above the letters.

Hint: Substitute a B for each T and an E for each Z that appears in the puzzle. Now use your logic skills to solve this puzzle.

3. F N Z   T Z K F   A B J R Z   F D

   N W P Z   W H   C D O ' X Z

   K R J X Z P   W K   W G K W P Z   J

   V J F N   T D D L....   F N Z X Z ' K

   K J H Z F C   W G   G O V T Z X K.

Cryptograms 4 and 5

Each letter below represents a different letter of the alphabet. To solve this puzzle, correctly substitute each letter and reveal a clever saying. If a letter appears more than once, it is like a variable and should be replaced by the same letter each time. Write your solution in the spaces above the letters.

Hint: In the first puzzle, substitute a T for each J. In the second puzzle, substitute an R for each J. Now use your logic skills to solve each puzzle.

4. JDTREVECNJDG   TH   Q

    HTVN   EU   JLN   JTCNH.

5. CZGL   REW'G   QIEG

    ZWBGLHJ   NBIJ—THGGHJ

    ABJO!

Cryptograms 6 and 7

Each letter below represents a different letter of the alphabet. To solve this puzzle, correctly substitute each letter and reveal a clever saying. If a letter appears more than once, it is like a variable and should be replaced by the same letter each time. Write your solution in the spaces above the letters.

Hint: In the first puzzle, substitute an N for each K and an R for each X. In the second puzzle, substitute an N for each M and a T for each P. Now use your logic skills to solve each puzzle.

6. K D O M X D G   K M S F B X Z   D X B

    F B O O B X   V I X   H I M X   L B D G O L.

7. C J P U   P Y J N U Y W R   E M Z D

    J A A   P U Y   J M K A Y R.

Ladder Logic 1

Change the word at the top of each ladder into the word on the bottom. You can change one letter on each step, and each step has to contain a real word.

add

sum

less

more

Ladder Logic 2

Change the word at the top of each ladder into the word at the bottom. You can change one letter on each step, and each step has to contain a real word.

black

white

nine

four

Matrix Logic 1

Mary, Molly, Mike, and Morris have been friends for many years. They all have different professions; one is a teacher, one is a doctor, one is a nurse, and one is a lawyer.

Use these clues and fill in the logic matrix below to match each person with his or her profession.

- Morris and Molly planned a birthday party for the teacher.

- On her way home, the doctor met Molly and they stopped off at the hospital to visit with the nurse.

- Morris is afraid he will miss most of the party because he has to work the 3-to-11 shift at work.

	Teacher	Doctor	Nurse	Lawyer
Mary				
Molly				
Mike				
Morris				

Matrix Logic 2

Four friends, Alice, Betty, Cathie, and Donna, each had a dog for a pet. The dogs were an Afghan hound, a beagle, a collie, and a dachshund. Use these clues and fill in the logic matrix below to help you match each person with her dog.

- None of the girls had a dog whose breed started with the same letter as her name.

- Betty's dog played with the Afghan hound and the dachshund at the park.

- Donna's dog was larger than the beagle.

- Cathie sometimes called her friend's dachshund "hot dog"!

	Afghan	Beagle	Collie	Dachshund
Alice				
Betty				
Cathie				
Donna				

Name _____ Date _____

Matrix Logic 3

Juan, Maria, and Carla were born in either Central America or South America. They moved to the United States and now attend schools there. Each has a favorite subject.

- No two students were born in the same country or share the same favorite subject.

- Carla was born on a Caribbean island and loves reading about the past.

- The student whose favorite subject is science lived in South America; he came to the United States when he was five years old.

See if you can match the children with their favorite subjects and the countries in which they were born. Fill in the logic matrix below.

	Math	Science	Social Studies	Mexico	Puerto Rico	Brazil
Juan						
Maria						
Carla						

Matrix Logic 4

Andy, Betty, Carl, and Diane work in the following professions: one is an artist, one is a barber, one is a chef, and one is a dentist. They live in Albany, Boston, Chicago, or Denver. None of them work in a profession or live in a city that begins with the same first letter as their name.

- The dentist lives in the Midwest; she dated the artist while he was in college.

- Diane ate dinner at the chef's restaurant when she went skiing; she loved his cooking.

- Diane lives in a beautiful apartment with a view of the ocean.

- The artist went to school in Chicago.

See if you can match each of these people with a profession and the city he or she lives in. Fill in the logic matrix below.

	Artist	Barber	Chef	Dentist	Albany	Boston	Chicago	Denver
Andy								
Betty								
Carl								
Diane								

PART 2: Critical Thinking and Math

These exercises will help review mathematics concepts and skills while moving your students into an algebraic frame of mind.

Being able to compute fluently, make estimates, and understand mathematical operations is essential to success in advanced mathematics classes. Students should be able to explain how they arrived at a solution and to understand that there may be many other methods. They learn to see the usefulness of being efficient and accurate. They learn to generalize.

The activities in this chapter encourage students to:

- use order of operations, integers, and transformations to solve magic squares

- revisit averages and the concepts of greatest common factor and least common multiple

- analyze the relationship between change in shape and percent change

- practice trial and error

- assign variables and use algebraic symbols to solve puzzles

Math by the Year 1

On December 19, 1732, Benjamin Franklin first published *Poor Richard, An Almanack.* It was published for 25 years and sold an average of 10,000 copies yearly. It was one of the most popular publications of colonial America.

- Use all four numbers of the year—1, 7, 3, and 2—in any order to find the numbers 1 to 10. You can add, subtract, multiply, divide, use exponents, or use square roots. But remember, you must follow the order of operations. Write your answers in the space below.

Additional Challenge: How many of the numbers between 11 and 20 can you calculate? Write your answers in the space below.

19

Math by the Year 2

On May 5, 1961, Alan Bartlett Shepard, Jr., became the first American in space. He made a successful suborbital flight aboard the Project Mercury capsule *Freedom Seven.*

- Use the numbers of the year—1, 9, 6, and 1—in any order to find the numbers 1 to 10. You can add, subtract, multiply, divide, use exponents, or use square roots. But remember, you must follow the order of operations. Write your answers in the space below.

Additional Challenge: How many of the numbers between 11 and 20 can you calculate? Write your answers in the space below.

Challenge to 100

Use all 9 digits from 1 to 9 to represent 100. You may add, subtract, multiply, and/or divide. Remember to use the order of operations! The digits may be arranged in any order and digits may be combined to form two-digit numbers. (For example, the 5 and the 6 may be combined to form the number 56.) See how many different ways you can find to make 100.

A Magic Square

Place the digits –4, –3, –2, –1, 0, 1, 2, 3, and 4 in the square below so that the sum along any row, column, or diagonal is 0. See how many solutions you can find.

Menu in the Cafeteria

On September 1, the school cafeteria served pizza, cheeseburgers, and taco salad. While planning meals for the year, the cafeteria staff decided to serve pizza every 4 days, cheeseburgers every 6 days, and taco salad every 8 days.

- Will these three meals be served together again in September?

- When is the next time all three will be served together?

- Explain how you solved this problem.

*What a Connection!

The numbers in the chart below are connected in a special way. The * symbol stands for that connection. Use the computations that have been done for you to fill in the missing numbers in the chart. Discover what the connection is.

What expression would you use to define the connection between the numbers in the chart? Write your answer in the space below.

*	2	3	4	5	6	8
2					6	
3		3				
4				20		
5						
6			12			
8				24		

$$3 * 3 = 3$$
$$6 * 4 = 12$$
$$4 * 5 = 20$$
$$8 * 6 = 24$$
$$2 * 6 = 6$$

Erica's Goal

At the beginning of the season, Erica told her basketball coach that her goal was to average 15 points per game. Her team plays an 8-game season. The table shows the points Erica scored in the first 7 games she played.

Game	1	2	3	4	5	6	7
Points Erica scored	11	18	10	17	11	15	20

- How many points does Erica need to score in her final game to reach her goal?

- Do you think it's possible for Erica to reach her goal? Explain your answer.

The Circle Problem

The radius of a circle is decreased by 10%.

- Does the area of the circle also decrease by 10%?

- If the area changes by a number other than 10%, what is the change?

- Does the circumference of the circle decrease by 10%?

- If the circumference changes by a number other than 10%, what is the change?

The Rectangle Problem

The length of a rectangle (the rectangle is **not** a square) is increased by 20%, but its width is decreased by 20%. The length of the rectangle is greater than the width.

- How did this change affect the area? Did the area increase, decrease, or remain the same?

- If the area changes, by what percent does it change?

Use the rectangle below to help you solve the problem—try some examples.

Mystery Numbers 1

I am thinking of 3 whole numbers. Use these clues to find the values of the three mystery numbers.

# # #

Clue #1

The middle number is 3 times the smallest number.

Clue #2

The largest number is 6 more than the middle number.

Clue #3

The sum of my 3 numbers is 34.

- What are the 3 numbers?

- Explain how you solved this problem.

Mystery Numbers 2

I am thinking of 3 whole numbers. Use these clues to find the values of the three mystery numbers.

# # #

Clue #1

The smallest number is a prime number that is $\frac{1}{6}$ the size of the middle number.

Clue #2

The largest number is 8 times the size of the smallest number.

Clue #3

The average of the 3 numbers is 15.

- What are the 3 numbers?

- Explain how you solved this problem.

Mystery Numbers 3

I am thinking of 3 whole numbers. Use these clues to find the values of the three mystery numbers.

# # #

Clue #1

The smallest number is the cube root of the largest number.

Clue #2

The middle number is $\frac{1}{3}$ the size of the largest number.

Clue #3

The smallest number is the square root (also $\frac{1}{3}$) of the middle number.

Clue #4

The average of the 3 numbers is 13.

- What are the 3 numbers?

- Explain how you solved this problem.

PART 3: Probability, Statistics, and Critical Thinking

Students are bombarded by data—in books and newspapers and on the Internet. If they don't understand how to organize and analyze data, they cannot make sense of it. Learning to judge the worth of statistical information and comprehend probability is central to the mathematics curriculum.

The activities in this chapter help students take a critical look at how to use the shape of the data (in graphs) to explain everyday occurrences. Students learn to understand probability and what it means to make valid statistical comparisons. The chapter opens with problems that make connections between geometry and probability: the greater the area, the greater the probability of occurence.

Students review fractions, number theory, and probability. They are encouraged to use their knowledge of combinations and permutations to think critically about advertising claims: How many choices are there? What are the chances of winning?

Each graph describes change over a period of time. Students learn that the shape of a graph tells a story.

Finally, students use real-world problems to explore probability.

Hitting the Target 1

ABCD is a square. Use the diagram to answer the questions below.

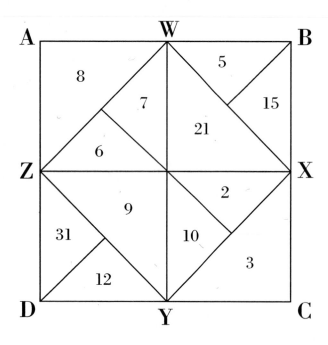

Point W bisects $\overline{AB}$.

Point X bisects $\overline{BC}$.

Point Y bisects $\overline{DC}$.

Point Z bisects $\overline{AD}$.

If we threw darts at this target, what is the probability that we would hit

- an even number?

- a prime number?

- a number that is divisible by 3?

- a number that is divisible by both 3 and 9?

- a number that is divisible by 6?

         10-Minute Critical-Thinking Activities for Algebra

Hitting the Target 2

This is a game board for a dart game. Four different players each choose one of the colors: red, yellow, green, or blue. When they hit their target color, they receive a point. If they hit an opponent's color, then the opponent gets the point.

- What is the probability that red will win? Yellow? Green? Blue?

- Is this game fair? Why or why not?

- How could you change the rules to make this a fair game?

Red	Yellow	Blue	Green
	Yellow		
Blue	Red		
	Blue	Red	Yellow
Green	Red		
	Yellow		

Pizza Pick

Pannini's Pizza Parlor advertises that you could get a pizza from them once a week for over two years and never have exactly the same pizza twice!

- Do you think this is an exaggeration?

- Explain your answer.

Type of Crust	Sizes	Toppings
Thin	Small	cheese pepperoni chicken ground beef sausage
Regular	Medium	green pepper onion sun-dried tomato eggplant anchovies
Deep Dish	Large	olives mushrooms spinach pineapple

The Batting Order

You are the manager of a baseball team. How many different ways can you set up your batting order using all nine players on your team?

Use the space below to explain how you solved this problem.

A Triple-Dip Ice Cream Cone

Sweeney's Sweet Shoppe has 25 different flavors of homemade ice cream. If you ordered a triple-dip cone with 3 different flavors of ice cream, how many different combinations of cones are possible? It doesn't matter where the flavor is on the cone—vanilla on top, chocolate in the middle, and strawberry on the bottom would be the same as chocolate on top, strawberry in the middle, and vanilla on the bottom.

Use the space below to explain how you solved this problem.

A Case of Area and Perimeter

You are rolling one standard die containing the numbers 1, 2, 3, 4, 5, and 6 to find the value of *x*.

What is the probability that

- the area of this rectangle will be greater than 50?

- the perimeter will be less than 30?

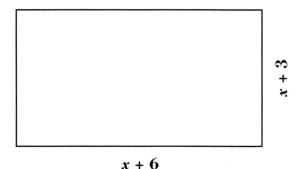

x + 3

x + 6

Are the Odds with You?

A state lottery used to draw six numbers from the numbers 1 to 52. The new lottery draws six numbers from the numbers 1 to 48. To announce the change, the lottery office published the following ad:

The odds are with you!
You have almost doubled your chances of winning!

- What are the odds of matching all 6 numbers in the game using 52 numbers?

- What are the odds of matching all 6 numbers in the game using 48 numbers?

- Do you think this ad is misleading? Are the odds really with you? Explain your thinking.

Name _____   Date _____

Let's Graph It 1

The *y*-axis (the vertical axis) of this graph represents a rate of speed, and the *x*-axis (the horizontal axis) represents the time that has elapsed.

- On a separate sheet of paper, write a story that might explain the graph.

- Design your own graph. Use the same axes to tell a different story.

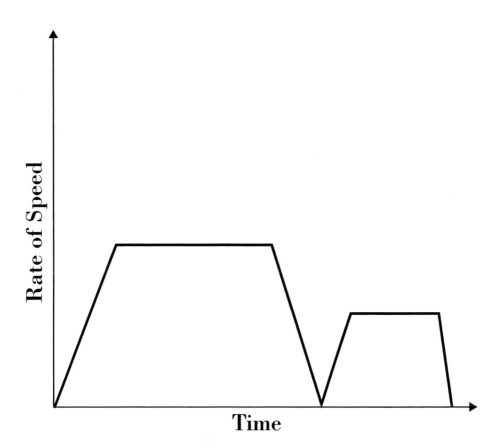

Let's Graph It 2

The Martins had a programmable thermostat installed to help save money on heating bills. At 6:00 A.M. the temperature is programmed to go up to 72°. It stays at that temperature until everyone leaves to go to school or work (8 A.M.); then it goes down to 65°. At 3:00 P.M. it goes back up to 72° and stays at that temperature until 10:00 P.M., when everyone goes to bed. Then it goes down to 65°. It stays at this temperature until the following morning, when the cycle repeats itself.

Draw a rough graph that visually represents the data. Use the (vertical) *y*-axis for temperature and the (horizontal) *x*-axis for time.

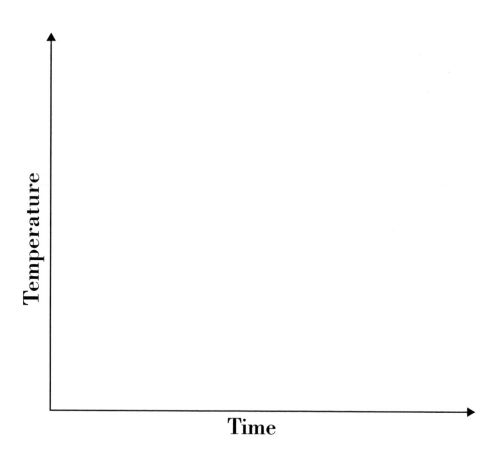

Let's Graph It 3

Examine each of these graphs. Use the horizontal and vertical axes to help you describe the data the graph represents. Write your answers on the lines below.

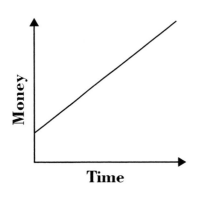

Time

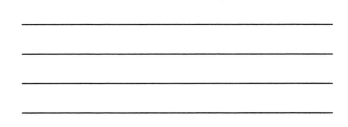

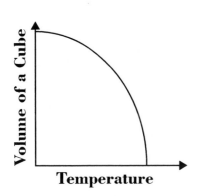

Temperature

Design your own graph below to show your height from birth to your current age. Be sure to label each axis. Describe the graph's shape.

PART 4: Proportional Reasoning, Problem Solving, and Critical Thinking

When students solve problems, they engage in tasks for which the solution methods are not known in advance. To solve the problem, students draw from previous knowledge. Through this process, they develop mathematical understanding. The National Council of Teachers of Mathematics defines problem solving as a process goal, distinct from a student's strategy to find an answer. When a teacher asks "Did anyone get a different answer? Did anyone solve the problem a different way?" students learn that there might be more than one answer to a problem and that there is certainly more than one way to solve it.

The problems in this chapter show students how to use algebra to solve problems. Proportional reasoning becomes a powerful problem-solving tool. Several puzzles pose an alternative to linear paper-and-pencil problem-solving strategies. Students learn to use visual clues to find creative solutions.

Name _____ Date _____

How Tall Is Josh?

O n the first day of school a group of friends met in the courtyard. The others looked at Josh and said "Wow! Did you grow this summer!"

"How tall are you now?" they asked.

Josh liked puzzles so he answered, "My height is 48 inches more than $\frac{1}{3}$ my height."

- How tall is Josh?

- How did you solve this problem?

43   *10-Minute Critical-Thinking Activities for Algebra*

The King and His Rubies

A king decided to share his collection of precious rubies with his three daughters. He gave his oldest daughter, Clara, 20% of the rubies. He gave Harriet, his middle daughter, 25% of those that were left. He gave his youngest daughter, Melissa, 30% of the remaining rubies. After each daughter had received her share, the king saw that there were 21 rubies left in his collection.

- How many rubies did the king have in his collection to begin with?

- How many did each daughter receive?

- Explain how you solved this problem. What problem-solving method did you use?

The Race

Carlos and Clyde challenged each other to a 140-mile motorcycle race (70 miles going west and then 70 miles east, returning to the starting position). Carlos traveled at a constant speed of 60 mph going west but returned at a constant speed of only 40 mph. Clyde traveled at a constant speed of 50 mph in each direction.

- Was the race a tie?

- If not, who won the race?

- How much time did it take each participant to finish the race?

- Explain how you solved this problem.

The Bumblebee Concert

Carmine had tickets to the Bumblebee Concert that began at 7:00 P.M. Carmine figured that if he took the highway from his house, he could average 60 miles per hour and get there $\frac{1}{2}$ hour early. If he took the streets, there would be less traffic, but he would average only about 30 miles per hour. This route would get him there 20 minutes late.

- Use this information to calculate the distance between Carmine's house and the concert.

- Explain how you solved this problem.

A Class Party

For the class party, the entertainment committee has decided to make lemonade. The directions on a can of Lemony Lemonade say to use 1 part of Lemony Lemonade powder for every 3 parts of water. The committee wants to make 1 gallon of lemonade (128 oz).

- How much water and how much mix will they need?

- Explain how you solved this problem.

Deer in the Forest

In an effort to keep track of the deer population, rangers tagged 500 deer and then released them back to the forest. About two months later they sighted 750 deer; 50 of them were tagged.

- Based on this data, how many deer might the rangers predict are in this area of the forest?

- How did you solve this problem?

- Do you think this method of "counting" is always accurate? Why or why not?

48
10-Minute Critical-Thinking Activities for Algebra

How High Is That Tree?

Carmen, who is 60 inches tall, casts an 8-foot shadow.

- At the same time and place, how long a shadow would a 35-foot tree cast?

- If the tree casts a 40-foot shadow, how tall is the tree?

- Explain how you solved these problems.

Model Trains and the Caboose

Did you know that different model trains are built to different standard scales?

- The O scale is 1:43
- The HO scale is 1:87
- The N scale is 1:160
- The Z scale is 1:220

The Oregon, Pacific & Eastern Railroad had a caboose that was 35 feet long and weighed about 25 tons.

- Which of the scale models of this caboose would be the largest? Which would be the smallest? How do you know? Explain your reasoning.

- How long would a model caboose be in each of these scales?

The Mass of Money

Y ou have 8 coins. There are 7 of equal weight and 1 that is heavier than the others. You have a balance scale, but you can only use it to make two weighings.

- By dividing the coins into equal groups, it is possible to determine in only two weighings which of the coins is heavier. How? Explain your strategy below.

 10-Minute Critical-Thinking Activities for Algebra

Measuring Water from a Stream 1

On a camping trip, your family brought along only two pails to collect water from a nearby stream. You brought only a 5-quart pail (Pail A) and a 3-quart pail (Pail B).

Pail A   **Pail B**

5   3

- Using only these two pails, how can you measure exactly 6 quarts of water?

Use this table to organize your work.

My Steps	Pail A	Pail B

Measuring Water from a Stream 2

On a camping trip, your family brought along only two pails to collect water from a nearby stream. You brought a 7-quart pail (Pail A) and a 3-quart pail (Pail B).

Pail A   **Pail B**

- Using only these two pails, how can you measure exactly 1 quart of water?

Use this table to organize your work.

My Steps	Pail A	Pail B

Measuring Water from a Stream 3

On a camping trip, your family brought only two pails to collect water from a nearby stream. You brought an 11-quart pail (Pail A) and a 3-quart pail (Pail B).

Pail A   **Pail B**

11   3

- Using only these two pails, how can you measure exactly 2 quarts of water?

Use this table to organize your work.

My Steps	Pail A	Pail B

The Mystery Line

In this diagram, sections labeled with the same letter have the same length.

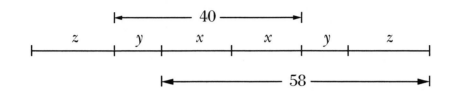

- Can you find the length of section *z*? Write your answer below.

Hint: It might help to set up a series of equations.

Nine Donkeys

Nine donkeys in a large pen are having a hard time getting along. Can you draw two squares so that each donkey has its own pen?

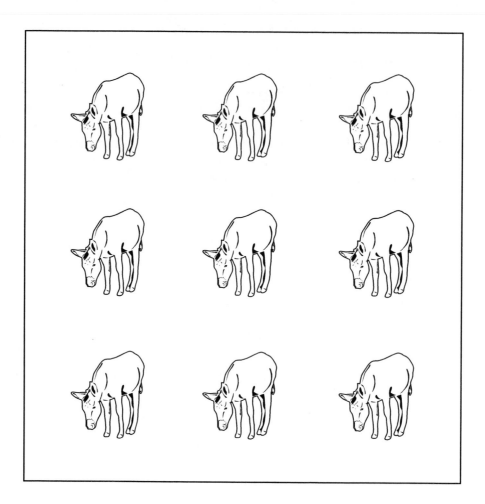

Toothpick Puzzle 1

Someone has arranged 12 toothpicks to form 4 squares.

- Move 3 toothpicks to form 3 squares instead of the 4 squares shown. Mark your changes on the drawing below.

- Can you find more than one solution to this problem?

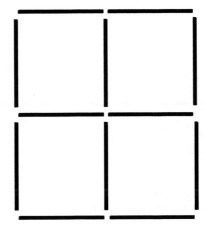

Toothpick Puzzle 2

Someone has arranged 28 toothpicks so that they form 10 squares.

- Move 4 toothpicks to form 7 squares instead of 10. Mark your changes on the drawing below.

- Can you find more than one solution to this problem?

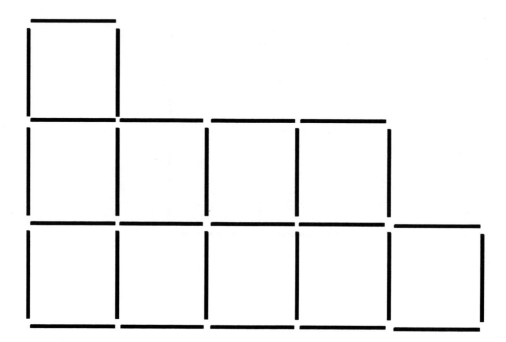

PART 5: Patterns, Functions, and Critical Thinking

Mathematics is the study of patterns. As students develop the ability to generalize, color patterns progress to number patterns and sequences. Students learn to predict the nth term of a sequence.

The problems in this chapter help students learn to use tables, graphs, words, and even rules to represent and analyze patterns. Some of the sequences have a twist—students look at a Fibonnaci-type sequence and use the pattern to develop a rule for all sequences of that type.

Number patterns, known as figurate numbers because their arrangements form polygons, can be quite challenging for students. Other problems in this chapter use geometric shapes to develop a pattern that can be generalized to a rule. Students are encouraged to use proportional reasoning and what they know to solve problems. By predicting the shape of a graph and then producing the graph, students learn how graphs and charts supply information and explain mathematical relationships.

Name _____ Date _____

What's the Pattern? 1

Find the next four terms of this sequence of numbers.

$$0, 3, 8, 15, \underline{\quad}, \underline{\quad}, \underline{\quad}, \underline{\quad}$$

Use the table to organize the data and to help you find a pattern. Then use the pattern to find the 20th term, the 50th term, and the *n*th term in the series.

Term	1	2	3	4	5	6	7	8	20	50	n
Number	0	3	8	15							

- How did you find the 5th, 6th, 7th, and 8th terms in this pattern?

- Did this same strategy work to find the 20th or 50th term? Why or why not?

- To generalize for the *n*th term you need to have a different strategy. What was it? How did you find this pattern?

What's the Pattern? 2

Find the next four terms of this sequence of numbers.

$$4, 7, 10, 13, \underline{\quad}, \underline{\quad}, \underline{\quad}, \underline{\quad}$$

Use the table to organize the data and to help you find a pattern. Then use the pattern to find the 20th term, the 50th term, and the nth term in the series.

Term	1	2	3	4	5	6	7	8	20	50	n
Number	4	7	10	13							

- How did you find the 5th, 6th, 7th, and 8th terms in this pattern?

- Did this same strategy work to find the 20th or 50th term? Why or why not?

- To generalize for the nth term you need to have a different strategy. What was it? How did you find this pattern?

What's the Pattern? 3

Find the next four terms of this sequence of numbers.

0, 8, 27, 64, ___, ___, ___, ___

Use the table to organize the data and to help you find a pattern. Then use the pattern to find the 20th term, the 50th term, and the nth term in this series.

Term	1	2	3	4	5	6	7	8	20	50	n
Number	0	8	27	64							

- How did you find the 5th, 6th, 7th, and 8th terms in this pattern?

- Did this same strategy work to find the 20th or 50th term? Why or why not?

- To generalize for the nth term you need to have a different strategy. What was it? How did you find this pattern?

What's the Pattern? 4

(a) 1, 2, 3, 5, 8, 13, ____, ____, ____

(b) 4, 6, 10, 16, 26, ____, ____, ____

(c) 3, 2, 5, 7, 12, ____, ____, ____

- Find the next three numbers in each of these sequences.

- What do each of these patterns have in common?

- Continue each pattern until it contains 10 terms. Find the sum of the first 10 terms of each sequence. Now multiply each 7th term by 11. Describe what you found. Why do you think this occurred?

- Design a new pattern with the same attributes as these patterns.

Building Blocks 1

W̶e have built three simple structures using blocks. The number of blocks needed to build each one has been filled in on the table below.

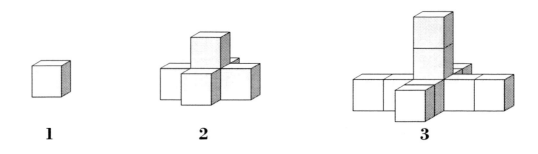

| 1 | 2 | 3 |

Structure	1	2	3	4	5	20	100	n
Number of Blocks	1	6	11					

- What would the 4th and 5th structures look like? How many blocks would you need to build them? Complete the table. Do you see a pattern?

- Could you use this pattern to help you find how many blocks would be needed to build the 20th structure? the 100th structure? the nth structure?

- Explain your reasoning.

10-Minute Critical-Thinking Activities for Algebra

Building Blocks 2

W̲e have built three simple structures using blocks. The number of blocks needed to build each one has been filled in on the table below.

 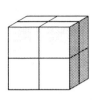 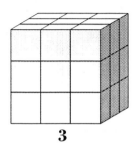

1   **2**   **3**

Structure	1	2	3	4	5	20	100	n
Number of Blocks	1	8	27					

- What would the 4th and 5th structures look like? How many blocks would you need to build them? Complete the table. Do you see a pattern?

- Could you use this pattern to help you find how many blocks would be needed to build the 20th structure? the 100th structure? the nth structure?

- Explain your reasoning.

10-Minute Critical-Thinking Activities for Algebra

How Many Triangles?

Examine the triangles and the table below and answer the following questions.

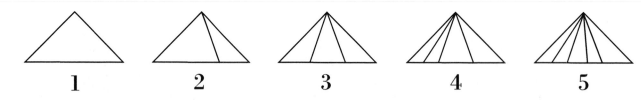

Triangle	1	2	3	4	5	6	10	20	50	100	n
# of Triangles	1	3	6								

- How many triangles are there in the 4th, 5th, and 6th triangles?

- Complete the table by finding a formula that will help you find the number of triangles no matter how many lines are added to the original triangle.

- Explain the formula you used to solve this problem.

The Area of a Rectangle

The area of a rectangle is 24 square units. The width of the rectangle varies as the length changes. Fill in the table below with the whole-number factors that show the inverse relationship between the length and width of this rectangle.

Length	1	2	3	4	5	6	7	8	9	10	11	12	13	14	15	16	17	18	19	20	21	22	23	24
Width	24	12			4.8																			

Use the data to predict the shape of the graph of this function. Write your answer on the line. _____

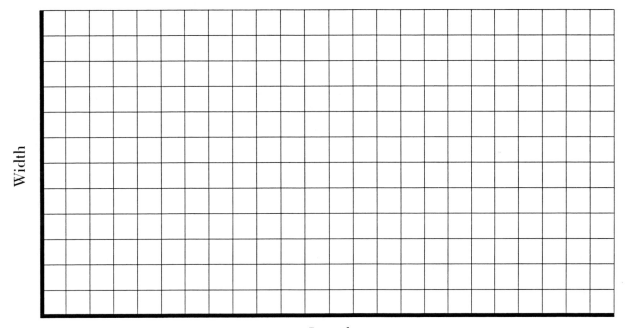

Length

Now calculate the non-whole-number factors. Use those values to make a graph. Round your answers to the nearest tenth. Describe the shape of your graph on the line. _____

The Triangle Problem

- Use the diagram to find out how many triangles there are in rows 3, 4, and 5.

- How many of each triangle will there be in row 6? in row 10? in row 50?

- How many of each triangle will there be in the *n*th row? On a separate sheet, explain how you solved this problem.

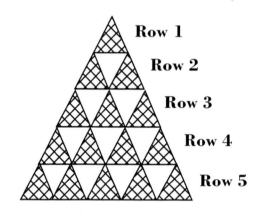

Row #	# of Patterned Triangles	# of White Triangles	Total # of Triangles in Row
1	1	0	1
2	2	1	3
3			
4			
5			
6			
10			
50			
n			

Patterns and More Patterns 1

Look at the arrangement of each group of tiles. The tiles have been arranged in a pattern that increases in size.

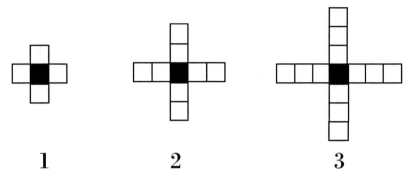

1   2   3

Answer the following questions on a separate sheet of paper.

- Predict the next two arrangements. Sketch the pattern.

- Predict how many tiles will be in the 20th arrangement. How many of the tiles will be white? How many of the tiles will be black?

- Predict how many tiles will be in the 50th arrangement. How many of the tiles will be white? How many of the tiles will be black?

- How many tiles will be in the nth arrangement? How many will be white? How many will be black? Explain how you solved this problem.

Patterns and More Patterns 2

Look at the arrangement of each group of tiles. The tiles have been arranged in a pattern that increases in size.

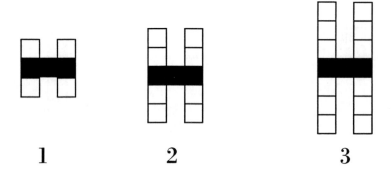

1   2   3

- Predict how many tiles will be in the 20th arrangement. How many of the tiles will be white? How many of the tiles will be black?

- Predict how many tiles will be in the 50th arrangement. How many of the tiles will be white? How many of the tiles will be black?

- How many tiles will be in the *n*th arrangement? How many will be white? How many will be black? Explain how you solved this problem.

Name _____   Date _____

Triangular Numbers

A figurate number is a number you can picture as an arrangement of equally spaced points. A figurate number has a definite shape. You can use equally spaced dots to draw a figurate number for any polygon. The first term of every figurate number is 1.

Think of a **triangular number** as an array of dots in the shape of a triangle. Look at the *series* of triangles below. Notice that you can draw the first triangle with 1 dot, you can draw the second triangle with 3 dots, and so on.

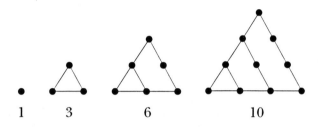

Use the information you have to find how many dots you will need for the 5th, 10th, 20th, and 100th triangle in the series. Complete the table.

	1st	2nd	3rd	4th	5th	10th	20th	100th	nth
Triangular Number	1	3	6	10					

Do you see a pattern that might help you find *any* triangular number? In the space below, write a formula that describes the pattern you see.

Pentagonal Numbers

A figurate number is a number you can picture as an arrangement of equally spaced points. A figurate number has a definite shape. You can use equally spaced dots to draw a figurate number for any polygon. The first term of every figurate number is 1.

Think of a **pentagonal number** as an array of dots in the shape of a pentagon. Look at the *series* of pentagons below. Notice that you can draw the first pentagon with 1 dot, you can draw the second pentagon with 5 dots, and so on.

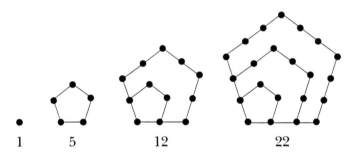

Use the information you have to find how many dots you will need for the 5th, 10th, 20th, and 100th pentagon in the series. Complete the table.

	1st	2nd	3rd	4th	5th	10th	20th	100th	n^{th}
Pentagonal Number	1	5	12	22					

Do you see a pattern that might help you find *any* pentagonal number? In the space below, write a formula that describes the pattern you see.

Hexagonal Numbers

Afigurate number is a number you can picture as an arrangement of equally spaced points. A figurate number has a definite shape. You can use equally spaced dots to draw a figurate number for any polygon. The first term of every figurate number is 1.

Think of a **hexagonal number** as an array of dots in the shape of a hexagon. Look at the *series* of hexagons below. Notice that you can draw the first hexagon with 1 dot, you can draw the second hexagon with 6 dots, and so on.

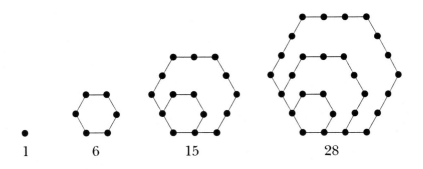

Use the information you have to find how many dots you will need for the 5th, 10th, 20th, and 100th hexagon in the series. Complete the table.

	1st	2nd	3rd	4th	5th	10th	20th	100th	n^{th}
Hexagonal Number	1	6	15	28					

Do you see a pattern that might help you find *any* hexagonal number? In the space below, write a formula that describes the pattern you see.

Octagonal Numbers

A figurate number is a number you can picture as an arrangement of equally spaced points. A figurate number has a definite shape. You can use equally spaced dots to draw a figurate number for any polygon. The first term of every figurate number is 1.

Think of an **octagonal number** as an array of dots in the shape of an octagon. Look at the *series* of octagons below. Notice that you can draw the first octagon with 1 dot, you can draw the second octagon with 8 dots, and so on.

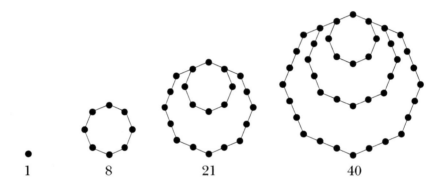

1   8   21   40

Use the information you have to find how many dots you will need for the 5th, 10th, 20th, and 100th octagon in the series. Complete the table.

	1st	2nd	3rd	4th	5th	10th	20th	100th	nth
Octagonal Number	1	8	21	40					

Do you see a pattern that might help you find *any* octagonal number? In the space below, write a formula that describes the pattern you see.

Answer Key

Part 1: Critical Thinking and Logic

Choices for Lunch (page 2)

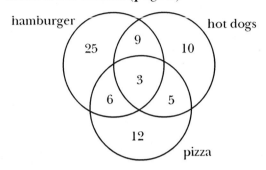

What Flavor Do You Like? (page 3)

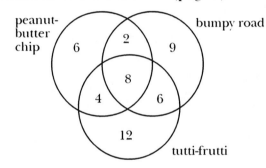

The Mystery Venn (page 4)

The numbers in circle A are all multiples of 9; the numbers in circle B are all multiples of 6; the numbers in the intersection are multiples of both 9 and 6.

Where Were They Born? (page 5)

In the innermost circle (California): Leonardo DiCaprio, Cameron Diaz, Marion Jones; in the middle circle (U.S.A.): George Foreman, Andy Rooney, Oprah Winfrey, Dr. Martin Luther King, Jr.; in the outermost circle (The World): Rod Stewart, Edward Teller, David Bowie, Vidal Sassoon, Princess Caroline; outside all the circles: E.T.

Mystery Regions (page 6)

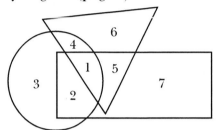

Cryptogram 1 (page 7)

1. The one way to be successful is to get on your "try"- cycle.

Cryptogram 2 (page 8)

2. "Can you do addition?" the White Queen asked. "What's one and one and one and one and one and one and one and one and one and one?" "I don't know," said Alice. "I lost count." Lewis Carroll

Cryptogram 3 (page 9)

3. The best place to hide if you're scared is inside a math book. . . . There's safety in numbers.

Cryptograms 4 and 5 (page 10)

4. Trigonometry is a sine of the times.
5. Math isn't just another four-letter word!

Cryptograms 6 and 7 (page 11)

6. Natural numbers are better for your health.
7. Math teachers know all the angles.

Ladder Logic 1 (page 12)

Possible solutions: add, aid, aim, him, hum, sum; less, mess, moss, most, post, port, pore, more

Ladder Logic 2 (page 13)

Possible solutions: black, slack, slick, slice, spice,
spine, shine, whine, white;
nine, fine, find, fond, food, fool, foul, four

Matrix Logic 1 (page 14)

	Teacher	Doctor	Nurse	Lawyer
Mary	X	O	X	X
Molly	X	X	X	O
Mike	O	X	X	X
Morris	X	X	O	X

Matrix Logic 2 (page 15)

	Afghan	Beagle	Collie	Dachshund
Alice	X	X	X	O
Betty	X	X	O	X
Cathie	X	O	X	X
Donna	O	X	X	X

Matrix Logic 3 (page 16)

	Math	Science	Social Studies	Mexico	Puerto Rico	Brazil
Juan	X	O	X	X	X	O
Maria	O	X	X	O	X	X
Carla	X	X	O	X	O	X

Matrix Logic 4 (page 17)

	Artist	Barber	Chef	Dentist	Albany	Boston	Chicago	Denver
Andy	X	X	O	X	X	X	X	O
Betty	X	X	X	O	X	X	O	X
Carl	O	X	X	X	O	X	X	X
Diane	X	O	X	X	X	O	X	X

Part 2: Critical Thinking and Math

Math by the Year 1 (page 19)

There are many different ways to solve each problem. These are some possible answers:

$7 - (3 + 2 + 1) = 1$

$[7 - (3 + 2)] \times 1 = 2$

$\dfrac{7 - 3}{2} + 1 = 3$

$\dfrac{7 - 3}{1^2} = 4$

$7 - 3 + 2 - 1 = 5$

$7 - \dfrac{3}{2 + 1} = 6$

$(7 \div 1^3) \times 1 = 7$

$7 + \dfrac{3}{2 + 1} = 8$

$7 + 2 \times 1^3 = 9$

$(7 + 3) \div 1^2 = 10$

Additional Challenge:

$7 + 3 + 1^2 = 11$

$7 + 3 + 2^1 = 12$

$7 + 1 + 3 + 2 = 13$

$7 \times 2 \div 1^3 = 14$

$7 \times 2 + 1^3 = 15$

$7 \times 2 + (3 - 1) = 16$

$7 \times 2 + 3^1 = 17$

$7 \times 3 - (2 + 1) = 18$

$7 \times 3 - 2 \times 1 = 19$

$7 \times 3 - 1^2 = 20$

Math by the Year 2 (page 20)

Some of the many ways to solve each problem are listed below. *Note:* Before assigning the problems, decide whether it might be acceptable to use the squares and square roots in the answers. Two of the solutions below, for example, require raising the number to the second power.

$\dfrac{1^9}{1^6} = 1$

$1^9 + 1^6 = 2$

$\dfrac{9 - 6}{1} \times 1 = 3$

$\dfrac{9 - 6 + 1}{1} = 4$

$9 - 6 + 1 + 1 = 5$

$1^9 + 6 - 1 = 6$

$1^9 + 6 \times 1 = 7$

$1^9 + 6 + 1 = 8$

$1^6 + 9 - 1 = 9$

$\dfrac{1^6 + 9}{1} = 10$

Additional Challenge:

$(9 + 1) + 1^6 = 11$

$[9 \times (1 + 1)] - 6 = 12$

$(\dfrac{6^2}{\sqrt{9}} + 1) \div 1 = 13$

$\dfrac{6^2}{\sqrt{9}} + 1 + 1 = 14$

$9 + 6 \times \dfrac{1}{1} = 15$

$\dfrac{9 + 1 + 6}{1} = 16$

$9 + 1 + 6 + 1 = 17$

$9 \times (1^6 + 1) = 18$

$\sqrt{9} \times 6^1 + 1 = 19$

$\sqrt{9} \times 6 + (1 + 1) = 20$

Challenge to 100 (page 21)

One possible solution: $1 + 2 + 3 + 4 + 5 + 6 + 7 + (8 \times 9) = 100$

A Magic Square (page 22)

Multiple solutions are possible using transformations. One possible solution:

-3	2	1
4	0	-4
-1	-2	3

Menu in the Cafeteria (page 23)

Use least common multiples to find that these items will be served on days that are multiples of 24. All three will be served on September 25 and again on October 19.

*What a Connection! (page 24)

The * symbol represents the least common multiple of both numbers.

✱	2	3	4	5	6	8
2	2	6	4	10	6	8
3	6	3	12	15	6	24
4	4	12	4	20	12	8
5	10	15	20	5	30	40
6	6	6	12	30	6	24
8	8	24	8	40	24	8

Erica's Goal (page 25)

To attain her goal (an average of 15 points per game), Erica has to score a total of 120 points. After seven games she has scored a total of 102 points. Erica needs 18 points to achieve her goal. There are a number of ways to solve this problem. Encourage students to share solutions and their problem-solving methods.

The Circle Problem (page 26)

No, the area decreases by more than 10%; it will always decrease by 19%. The circumference does change by 10%.

The Rectangle Problem (page 27)

The area does change; the new area is less than the original area. It decreases by 4%.

Mystery Numbers 1 (page 28)

Let n = the smallest number; $3n$ = the middle number; $3n + 6$ = the largest number.

$n + 3n + 3n + 6 = 34$; $7n + 6 = 34$; $n = 4$, $3n = 12$, $3n + 6 = 18$.

The numbers are 4, 12, and 18.

Mystery Numbers 2 (page 29)

Let n = the smallest number; $6n$ = the middle number; $8n$ = the largest number.

$\frac{8n + 6n + n}{3} = 15$; $n = 3$; $6n = 18$; $8n = 24$

The numbers are 3, 18, and 24.

Mystery Numbers 3 (page 30)

Let n = the smallest number; $3n$ = the middle number; $9n$ = the largest number.

$\frac{n + 3n + 9n}{3} = 13$; $n = 3$; $3n = 9$; $9n = 27$

The numbers are 3, 9, and 27.

Part 3: Probability, Statistics, and Critical Thinking

Hitting the Target 1 (page 32)

1. 3/8; 2. 3/8; 3. 9/16; 4. 1/8; 5. 1/8

Hitting the Target 2 (page 33)

1. Red: 7/24 or 29-1/6% chance of winning; blue: 1/4 or 25% chance of winning; yellow: 5/24 or 20-5/6% chance of winning; green: 1/4 or 25% chance of winning.
2. The game is not fair because the person who chooses red has the greatest chance of winning and the person who chooses yellow has the least chance. A fair game gives each player an equal chance of winning. Target colors must be of equal area and evenly distributed on the board.

Pizza Pick (page 34)

Choosing only one type of crust, one size, and only one type of topping, the number of choices are $3 \times 3 \times 14$ or 126 choices. The number of choices increases if you choose two-topping or three-topping pizzas. 126 weeks is approximately 2.4 years.

The Batting Order (page 35)

The number of different ways to organize the batting order is 9! or 362,880 ways.

A Triple-Dip Ice Cream Cone (page 36)

$_{25}C_3 = \frac{25 \cdot 24 \cdot 23}{3 \cdot 2 \cdot 1} = 2{,}300$ possible triple-dip cones.

A Case of Area and Perimeter (page 37)

The probability that the area will be greater than 50 is 2/3. The probability that the perimeter will be less than 30 is 1/3.

Roll of Die	1	2	3	4	5	6
Area	28	40	54	70	88	108
Perimeter	22	26	30	34	38	42

Are the Odds with You? (page 38)

The odds of matching all six numbers with choices 1–52 are 1 in 20,358,520. The odds of matching all six numbers with choices 1–48 are 1 in 12,271,512. The odds of winning have increased substantially, but the odds are certainly not with you. To give you some perspective of the odds, imagine that paper cups have been placed side by side and upside down all the way from Chicago, IL, to Atlanta, GA. The winning number has been placed in one of these cups. Your chances of choosing the correct cup are the same as the probability of your matching all 6 of the numbers in the 48-number lottery!

Let's Graph It 1 (page 39)

Answers will vary. Possible answer: A car starts up and reaches a speed of 40 mph. It comes to a halt at a stop sign, then accelerates to 25 miles an hour. When it reaches its destination, it stops and parks.

Let's Graph It 2 (page 40)

Possible answer:

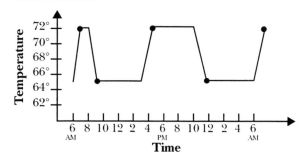

Let's Graph It 3 (page 41)

Answers will vary. The first graph could represent money in a savings account drawing interest over a period of years. The second graph could represent the volume of an ice cube as temperature rises.

Part 4: Proportional Reasoning, Problem Solving, and Critical Thinking

How Tall Is Josh? (page 43)

Where h = Josh's height, $\frac{1}{3}h + 48 = h$; $h = 72"$. Josh is 6 feet tall.

The King and His Rubies (page 44)

By working backward or by converting percents to fractions, students calculate that after Clara received her $\frac{1}{5}$ share, $\frac{4}{5}$ of the rubies were left. Harriet received $\frac{1}{4}$ of the $\frac{4}{5}$ that were left, or another $\frac{1}{5}$ (leaving $\frac{3}{5}$ of the total). Melissa received $\frac{3}{10}$ of the $\frac{3}{5}$ rubies that were left ($\frac{3}{10}$ of $\frac{3}{5}$), or $\frac{9}{50}$ of the rubies. Together, Clara, Harriet, and Melissa received $\frac{1}{5}$ share + $\frac{1}{5}$ share + $\frac{9}{50}$ share. Expressed with a common denominator, the daughters received $\frac{10}{50} + \frac{10}{50} + \frac{9}{50}$, or $\frac{29}{50}$. The daughters received 29 of 50 rubies; the king was left with 21 of the 50 he started with.

The Race (page 45)

One way to solve this problem: Carlos took $1\frac{1}{6}$ hours going and $1\frac{3}{4}$ hours coming back. His total time was $2\frac{11}{12}$ hours or 2 hours and 55 minutes. Clyde took $1\frac{2}{5}$ hours each way for a total time of $2\frac{4}{5}$ hours or 2 hours and 48 minutes. Clyde won the race by 7 minutes.

The Bumblebee Concert (page 46)

One way to solve the problem is to set up the distance (d) to the concert as an equality: $d = (mph) \times (t)$.

Substitute the values given for each route.
(60 miles/hour) $\times$ (t – 30 minutes) = (60 miles/hour) $\times$ (t + 20 minutes)

$d = 50$ miles

A Class Party (page 47)

1 part powder to 3 parts water means that $\frac{1}{4}$ of the mixture is powder and $\frac{3}{4}$ of the mixture is water. $\frac{1}{4}$ of 128 oz. = 32 oz. of powder; $\frac{3}{4}$ of 128 oz. = 96 oz. water.

Deer in the Forest (page 48)

Solve this problem by setting up a proportion: If $\frac{50}{750} = \frac{500}{x}$, $x = 7,500$ deer. Although the solution assigns a whole number, students should understand that because it is based on the accuracy of the capture-recapture and sampling techniques, the number is only approximate.

How High Is That Tree? (page 49)

Use a proportional relationship to solve this problem. Convert the 60 inches to 5 feet. $\frac{5}{8} = \frac{35}{x}$; $x = 56$ feet. $\frac{5}{8} = \frac{x}{40}$; $x = 25$ feet.

Model Trains and the Caboose (page 50)

Ratios act like fractions. The ratio of the O-scale model to the caboose is 1:43. That means the real caboose is 43 times as long as the model and that the O-scale model is $\frac{1}{43}$ the length of the real caboose. The largest would be the O scale because 1 foot on the model is equivalent to only 43 feet on the actual train. The smallest would be the Z scale.

The O-scale model is $\frac{1}{43}$ of 35 feet ($\frac{1}{43}$ of 420 inches), or about 9.767 inches long.

The HO-scale model is $\frac{1}{87}$ of 35 feet ($\frac{1}{87}$ of 420 inches), or about 4.827 inches long.

The N-scale model is $\frac{1}{160}$ of 35 feet ($\frac{1}{160}$ of 420 inches), or about 2.625 inches long.

The Z-scale model is $\frac{1}{220}$ of 35 feet ($\frac{1}{220}$ of 420 inches), or about 1.909 inches long.

The Mass of Money (page 51)

Among the possible solutions:

Set aside two of the coins, and put the remaining six on a scale. If the scales balance, then one of the two coins set aside is the heavier coin. Discover which is heavier by weighing the two.

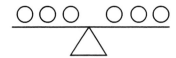

If they don't balance, examine the three coins on the depressed side of the scale. Set aside one of those coins, and weigh the remaining two. If the scales balance, then the coin that was set aside is heavier; if the scales do not balance, the side with the heavier coin is obvious.

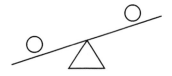

Measuring Water from a Stream 1 (page 52)

My Steps	Pail A	Pail B
Fill pail B.	0	3
Pour B into A.	3	0
Fill B.	3	3

Measuring Water from a Stream 2 (page 53)

My Steps	Pail A	Pail B
Fill pail A.	7	0
Pour A into B.	4	3
Empty B.	4	0
Pour A into B.	1	3

Measuring Water from a Stream 3 (page 54)

My Steps	Pail A	Pail B
Fill pail A.	11	0
Pour A into B.	8	3
Empty B.	8	0
Pour A into B.	5	3
Empty B.	5	0
Pour A into B.	2	3

The Mystery Line (page 55)

Use the information given to set up two equations.

$2x + y + z = 58$ and

$2x + y = 40$

Substitute 40 for $2x + y$ in the first equation:

$40 + z = 58$

$z = 18$

Nine Donkeys (page 56)

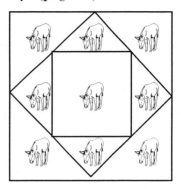

Toothpick Puzzle 1 (page 57)

Among the possible solutions:

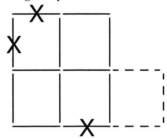

Toothpick Puzzle 2 (page 58)

Among the possible solutions:

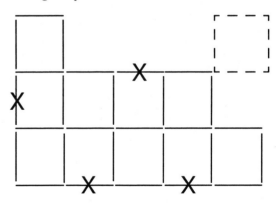

Part 5: Patterns, Functions, and Critical Thinking

What's the Pattern? 1 (page 60)

The next four terms are 24, 35, 48, 63. The differences between the terms are 3, 5, 7, 9, etc. This strategy is not practical for the 20th or the 50th term. It certainly will not generalize to the *n*th term. Let $t =$ the number of the term, then $t^2 - 1$ will generalize for any term of the pattern.

What's the Pattern? 2 (page 61)

The next four terms are 16, 19, 22, 25. The difference between the terms is 3. This strategy is not practical for the 20th or the 50th term. It certainly will not generalize to the *n*th term. Let $t =$ the number of the term, then $3t + 1$ will generalize for any term of the pattern.

What's the Pattern? 3 (page 62)

The next four terms are 125, 216, 343, 512. The pattern is the cube of the terms (counting numbers). Thus, term 20 would be 8,000, term 50 would be 125,000, term n would be t^3.

What's the Pattern? 4 (page 63)

These are Fibonnacci-type sequences—that is, the third number of the sequence is the sum of the first two, the fourth number of the sequence is the sum of the second and third, and so on.

(a) 21, 34, 55, 89; (b) 42, 68, 110, 178; (c) 19, 31, 50, 81

The sum of the first 10 numbers of the sequence is equal to the 7th term times 11.

Building Blocks 1 (page 64)

The formulas students find to solve for the pattern may vary.

Structure	4	5	20	100	n
Number of Blocks	16	21	96	496	$5(n-1)+1$

Building Blocks 2 (page 65)

The formulas students find to solve for the pattern may vary.

Structure	4	5	20	100	n
Number of Blocks	64	125	8,000	1,000,000	n^3

How Many Triangles? (page 66)

Triangle	1	2	3	4	5	6	10	20	50	100	n
# of Triangles	1	3	6	10	15	21	55	210	1,275	5,050	$\dfrac{n(n+1)}{2}$

The Area of a Rectangle (page 67)

L	1	2	3	4	5	6	7	8	9	10	11	12	13	14	15	16	17	18	19	20	21	22	23	24
W	24	12	8	6		4		3				2												1

Whole-number factors yield a linear graph. The other non-whole-number factors can be calculated and used to make a nonlinear graph.

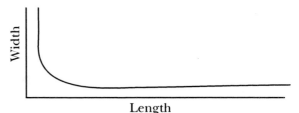

The Triangle Problem (page 68)

Row #	# of Patterned Triangles	# of White Triangles	Total # of Triangles in Row
1	1	0	1
2	2	1	3
3	3	2	5
4	4	3	7
5	5	4	9
6	6	5	11
10	10	9	19
50	50	49	99
n	n	$n-1$	$2n-1$

Patterns and More Patterns 1 (page 69)

The fourth arrangement will have 1 black tile in the center and 4 white tiles on each edge, for a total of $4(4) + 1$ tiles, or 17, 1 black and 16 white. The 5th arrangement will have 1 tile in the center and five tiles on each edge, $4(5) + 1$ tiles, or 21 tiles, 20 white and 1 black. The 20th arrangement will have $4(20) + 1$ or 81 tiles, 1 black and 80 white. The 50th will have $4(50) + 1$ or 101, 1 black and 100 white. The nth arrangement will have $4n + 1$ tiles, 1 black and $4n$ white.

Patterns and More Patterns 2 (page 70)

Each of the first three arrangements has a group of 3 black tiles in the center with 4 towers of white tiles, each having n tiles in the tower. So the third pattern has $3 + [4(3)]$ tiles or 15 tiles, 3 black and 12 white. The 20th arrangement will have $3 + [4(20)]$ or 83 tiles, 3 black and 80 white. The 50th will have $3 + [4(50)]$, or 203 tiles, 3 black and 200 white. The nth arrangement will have $3 + 4n$ tiles, 3 black and $4n$ white.

Triangular Numbers (page 71)

15, 55, 210, 5500, $\frac{n(n+1)}{2}$

* 1 is considered any figurate number because it satisfies the expression when it is substituted for n.

Pentagonal Numbers (page 72)

35, 145, 590, 14,950, $\frac{n(3n-1)}{2}$

* 1 is considered any figurate number because it satisfies the expression when it is substituted for n.

Hexagonal Numbers (page 73)

45, 190, 780, 19,900, $n(2n-1)$

* 1 is considered any figurate number because it satisfies the expression when it is substituted for n.

Octagonal Numbers (page 74)

65, 280, 1160, 29,800, $n(3n-2)$

* 1 is considered any figurate number because it satisfies the expression when it is substituted for n.

Share Your Bright Ideas with Us!

We want to hear from you! Your valuable comments and suggestions will help us meet your current and future classroom needs.

Your name_____Date_____

School name_____Phone_____

School address_____

City _____State _____Zip_____Phone number (_____)_____

Grade level taught_____Subject area(s) taught_____Average class size_____

Where did you purchase this publication?_____

Was your salesperson knowledgeable about this product?   Yes_____   No_____

What monies were used to purchase this product?

____School supplemental budget   ____Federal/state funding   ____Personal

Please "grade" this Walch publication according to the following criteria:

	A	B	C	D	F
Quality of service you received when purchasing	A	B	C	D	F
Ease of use	A	B	C	D	F
Quality of content	A	B	C	D	F
Page layout	A	B	C	D	F
Organization of material	A	B	C	D	F
Suitability for grade level	A	B	C	D	F
Instructional value	A	B	C	D	F

COMMENTS:_____

_____

What specific supplemental materials would help you meet your current—or future—instructional needs?

_____

Have you used other Walch publications? If so, which ones?_____

May we use your comments in upcoming communications?   ____Yes   ____No

Please **FAX** this completed form to **207-772-3105**, or mail it to:

Product Development, J. Weston Walch, Publisher, P. O. Box 658, Portland, ME 04104-0658

We will send you a **FREE GIFT** as our way of thanking you for your feedback. **THANK YOU!**